This book belongs to...

First published 1999 by Walker Books Ltd
87 Vauxhall Walk, London SE11 5HJ

© 1999 Lucy Cousins

Lucy Cousins font © 1999 Lucy Cousins

Maisy™. Maisy is a registered trademark of Walker Books Ltd, London

The right of Lucy Cousins to be identified as author/illustrator of this work has been
asserted by her in accordance with the Copyright, Designs and Patents Act 1988

Printed in China

British Library Cataloguing in Publication Data

A catalogue record for this book is available from the British Library

ISBN 978-0-7445-6924-7

www.walker.co.uk

www.maisyfun.com

Maisy and her Friends Colouring Book

by Lucy Cousins

WALKER BOOKS
AND SUBSIDIARIES
LONDON · BOSTON · SYDNEY · AUCKLAND

Maisy rides
the horse

Maisy feeds the lambs

Maisy pushes
her toy horse

Maisy goes sailing

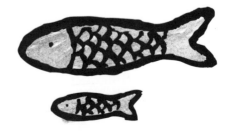

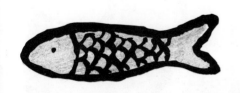

Maisy plays games

with her friends

tooty
toot

Maisy gives the

geese a drink

Maisy cleans

up the pigsty

Maisy flies her kite

Maisy plays music

with some friends

The ostrich and the peacock

bow to
Queen Maisy